The Pie-Eating Contest

CUSTOM

First published in 2009
by Wayland

This paperback edition published in 2010

Text copyright © Mick Gowar
Illustration copyright © François Hall

Wayland
338 Euston Road
London NW1 3BH

Wayland Australia
Level 17/207 Kent Street
Sydney, NSW 2000

Series Editor: Louise John
Cover design: Paul Cherrill
Design: D.R.ink
Consultant: Shirley Bickler

A CIP catalogue record for this book is available from the British Library.

ISBN 9780750255516 (hbk)
ISBN 9780750255554 (pbk)

Printed in China

Wayland is a division of Hachette Children's Books,
an Hachette Livre UK Company

The Pie-Eating Contest

Written by Mick Gowar
Illustrated by François Hall

WAYLAND

It was supper time in Cactus Thorn,
but Deputy Pete didn't feel like eating.

"It's your favourite — bacon and beans," said Sheriff Stan.

"I'm not hungry," said Pete.

"But it's the pie-eating contest on Saturday," said Sheriff Stan. "You're the champion. You need to keep up your strength!"

Deputy Pete sighed. "I'll go for
a walk. Walking always makes
me hungry."

"It's Deputy Pete," whispered
Dudley Dalton.
"Quick, put this sack over his
head," said Ma Dalton.

They grabbed Pete and tied him up. Then they took him to their shack in the woods.

"Let me go!" shouted Pete. "Help me!"

"I'll let you go on Saturday," said Ma Dalton. "Promise. As soon as my son Dudley has won the pie-eating contest."

"Can I have something to eat?" asked Pete.

"Yes," said Ma. "You can have bread and water."

13

"Is that all?" asked Pete.

"Yes," said Ma, and Dudley and Ma tucked into their pies.

Next morning, it was the same. "Can I have some breakfast, please?" asked Pete. "I'm hungry."

"You can have bread and water," said Ma Dalton.

All day long Pete's tummy rumbled and grumbled. He was starving!

"Do you want some supper?" asked Ma Dalton.

"Yes!" said Pete. "I'm SO hungry. What are we having?"

"Bread and water," said Ma Dalton.

19

Next morning Pete was
EVEN MORE hungry.

"Bye, Pete," said Ma Dalton.
"Dudley and I are off to
the contest!"

Pete had eaten nothing but bread and water for three days. He was so thin that his hands slipped out of the ropes Ma Dalton had tied him up with.

Pete ran all the way back to Cactus Thorn and was just in time for the pie-eating contest!

"Welcome back!" said Sheriff Stan. "Did your long walk make you hungry?"

"I'm so hungry I could eat a cow!" said Pete. "A cow pie!"

"Ready... Steady... EAT!"
The contest began.

Pete ate one pie. Then another. And another. He kept going and going until he had eaten all the pies on the table!

Dudley Dalton couldn't keep up with him. Ma Dalton was very cross indeed!

Sheriff Stan climbed up onto the stage. "And the winner of the pie-eating contest is…" he shouted. There was a drum roll. "…Deputy Pete!"

The crowd went wild.